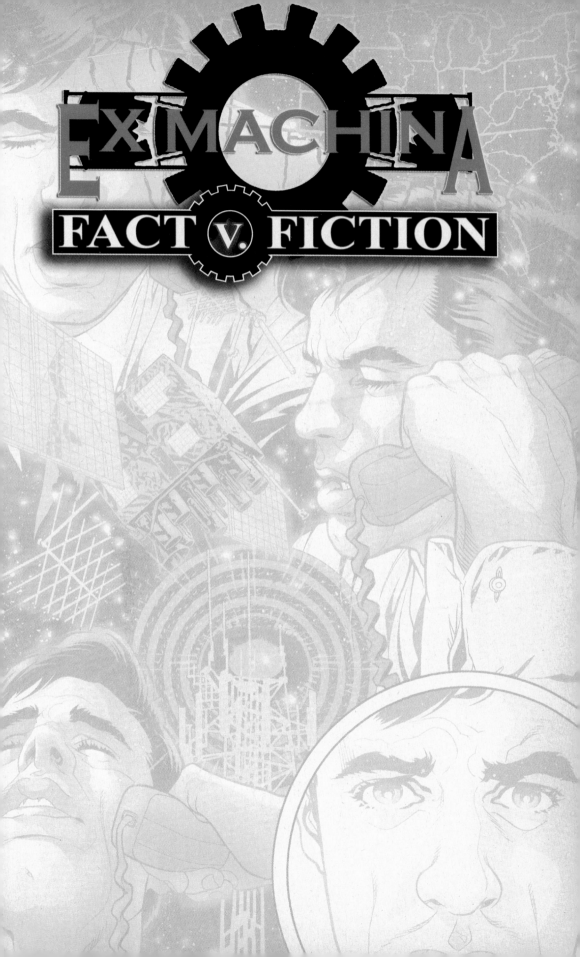

Brian K. Vaughan: Writes

Tony Harris: Pencils

Tom Feister with Karl Story**:** Inks

JD Mettler: Colors

Jared K. Fletcher: Letters

Larry Berry: Designs

Ex Machina created by Vaughan and Harris

LEGAL

Jim Lee, Editorial Director **John Nee,** VP—Business Development **Scott Dunbier,** Executive Editor
Ben Abernathy, Editor **Kristy Quinn,** Assistant Editor **Ed Roeder,** Art Director **Paul Levitz,** President & Publisher
Georg Brewer, VP—Design & DC Direct Creative **Richard Bruning,** Senior VP—Creative Director
Patrick Caldon, Executive VP—Finance & Operations **Chris Caramalis,** VP—Finance **John Cunningham,** VP—Marketing
Terri Cunningham, VP—Managing Editor **Stephanie Fierman,** Senior VP—Sales & Marketing **Alison Gill,** VP—Manufacturing
Rich Johnson, VP—Book Trade Sales **Hank Kanalz,** VP—General Manager, WildStorm
Lillian Laserson, Senior VP & General Counsel **Paula Lowitt,** Senior VP—Business & Legal Affairs
David McKillips, VP—Advertising & Custom Publishing **Gregory Noveck,** Senior VP—Creative Affairs
Cheryl Rubin, Senior VP—Brand Management **Jeff Trojan,** VP—Business Development, DC Direct **Bob Wayne,** VP—Sales

"For Ruth, my New York City." — Brian K. Vaughan

"I would like to dedicate this volume to two dear friends, Eric and his wife Mimi.

"They are first my friends and second my fans, but it didn't start out that way. It's a rare thing in the entertainment industry to meet folks at a show and become such fast friends, but that's what happened. Over the years you guys have supported me personally, professionally, and emotionally. You will alway have a fan in me."

— Tony Harris

"To Jack, my hope. To Sonya, my love."

-Tom Feiste

"To my wife Amy, for your love and white magic; to my mother Darlene, for teaching me that creativity and practicality can coexist; and to my father George, for teaching me that although it's possible to color completely within the lines, it is more interesting not to."

- JD Mettle

CHAPTER 1

EARTH TO HIZZONER.

TUESDAY, JULY 30, 2002

YOU ALL RIGHT, MAYOR HUNDRED?

I WAS SAYING THAT FORCING ME TO ATTEND THESE BUDGETARY MEETINGS MAKES ME WANT TO JUMP OFF A FUCKIN' *BUILDING*, AND YOU DISAPPEARED TO YOUR SAFE PLACE.

SORRY, COMMISH, BUT NOW THAT WE'VE FINALLY MANAGED TO *STABILIZE* THE ECONOMY, MY PRIMARY MISSION THIS QUARTER IS STEERING US TOWARDS SOMETHING RESEMBLING *RECOVERY.*

AND UNFORTUNATELY, THAT MEANS ASKING THE NYPD TO START *ENFORCING* STUFF LIKE 165.35.

COUSIN? YOU HAVE A *VISITOR.*

THAT MUST BE *HUNDRED,* THE LUCKY NUMBER.

I'VE BEEN *WAITING* FOR YOU...

THOSE YOUR "PSYCHIC POWERS" AT WORK?

NO, I JUST GOT OFF THE CELL WITH OUR YOUNG *ELLEN.*

SHE KINDLY INFORMED ME THAT YOU MIGHT BE STOPPING BY.

THEN YOU KNOW WHY I'M HERE.

FOR THE SAME REASON *HITLER* GASSED A HALF-MILLION OF MY ANCESTORS DURING THE DEVOURING, YES?

YOU GADJÉ DESPISE WHAT YOU DON'T UNDERSTAND, SO YOU HUNT AND OPPRESS US. WE'VE ENDURED SUCH PERSECUTION FOR CENTURIES, SO THIS COMES AS NO SURPRISE.

NICE TRY, ZEHALA, BUT WE BOTH KNOW THIS HAS NOTHING TO DO WITH YOU BEING A *GYPSY.*

PLEASE, THAT WORD HITS MY EARS LIKE *NIGGER.* I'VE READ HOW YOU LIKE RACIAL SLURS ON YOUR *PAINTINGS,* BUT I'D APPRECIATE IF YOU KEPT THEM OUT OF MY *HOME.*

THE PREFERRED TERM FOR MY PEOPLE-- 100,000 OF WHOM HAPPEN TO BE YOUR *CONSTITUENTS*-- IS *ROMA.*

I'M...I'M TERRIBLY SORRY.

HA, I KNEW IT! YOU CALL YOUR-SELF "INDEPENDENT," BUT I COULD SMELL THAT *LIBERAL GUILT* A MILE AWAY.

KEEP IT UP, AND YOU GET TO SEE HOW *CONSERVATIVE* I AM ON *CRIME*.

JUST BECAUSE YOU'RE GOOD AT READING PEOPLE DOESN'T MEAN YOU GET TO TAKE THEIR *MONEY*.

YOU THINK I *CHOSE* THIS SAD EXCUSE FOR A PROFESSION? WHEN I WAS A GIRL, I WANTED TO BE A MARINE BIOLOGIST... NOT A FUCKING *CLICHÉ*.

BUT I FOUND THAT I HAD A GIFT, AND I DECIDED TO USE IT TO *HELP* PEOPLE. AM I NOT ENTITLED TO MAKE A *LIVING* FOR MY SERVICES?

YEAH, THAT ROUTINE MAY WORK ON YOUR *MARKS*, BUT I WAS PRACTICALLY *RAISED* ON THE BOARDWALK.

I KNOW A *CON* WHEN I HEAR ONE.

THEN COME, IF YOU'RE SO IMMUNE TO MY CHARMS, YOU HAVE NO REASON NOT TO GIVE ME YOUR *HAND*...

IT WASN'T MY *IMAGINATION* THAT FORESAW THE PLANE HITTING THAT BUILDING.

HOLD ON.

YOU'RE SAYING YOU DIDN'T JUST PREDICT ELLEN'S DEATH...YOU PREDICTED ALL OF *9/11?*

NO, NOT ALL OF IT. MY WORK IS HARDLY A SCIENCE. BUT I SAW THE AIRCRAFT'S IMPACT, SAW THE SKYSCRAPER *COLLAPSE...*

WHAT?! WHY THE FUCK DIDN'T YOU *TELL* SOMEONE?

SO *NOW* YOU BELIEVE, DO YOU?

WHO WOULD HAVE LISTENED TO ME, MR. HUNDRED? ALL I WOULD HAVE DONE IS SET UP MY FAMILY AND ME FOR A LENGTHY *DETENTION* BY FEDERAL AUTHORITIES.

SO INSTEAD, I DID WHAT I COULD. I SAVED *ONE* LIFE... WHICH IS ONE MORE THAN THOSE IN THE GOVERNMENT WHO WERE *SUPPOSED* TO BE LOOKING OUT FOR US DID.

I WAS LOOKING OUT FOR US! IF I COULD HAVE BEEN THERE FROM THE *BEGINNING*, I...I...

I MADE IT BACK TO GROUND ZERO ABOUT NINETY MINUTES AFTER I DIVERTED THE *SECOND* PLANE, FORCED IT TO MAKE AN EMERGENCY LANDING.

THERE WASN'T A CIVIL ENGINEER ALIVE WHO THOUGHT THAT TOWER WOULD GO DOWN, BUT STILL, I...I TRIED TO HELP EVERYONE WHO WAS TRAPPED BY THE FIRE.

I TRIED TO CONVINCE THE JUMPERS TO HOLD ON, BUT... BUT *PEOPLE* DON'T LISTEN TO THE GODDAMN "GREAT MACHINE" THE WAY...

WHATEVER, I TRIED TO *CATCH* THEM, BUT THERE WERE SO MANY. I'M NOT THAT FAST, NOT THAT STRONG...

THIS WAS BEYOND US BOTH, MY FRIEND.

IT WAS *FATE* THAT CHOSE WHO LIVED AND DIED THAT DAY. WE CAN TRY TO WEIGHT HER WHEEL, BUT CHANCE ALWAYS GETS THE FINAL SPIN.

SHUT THE FUCK UP WITH THAT!

EITHER YOU'RE LYING ABOUT PREDICTING THE ATTACKS, WHICH MAKES YOU A CHARLATAN AND A...A *THIEF*, OR YOU'RE TELLING THE *TRUTH*, WHICH MAKES YOU A FUCKING ACCOMPLICE TO *MASS MURDER*.

FOR A MAN WHO IS HARDLY FREE OF *SIN*, YOU CERTAINLY ARE JUDGMENTAL.

YES, I CAN SEE YOUR *PAST* AS WELL AS YOUR FUTURE. I CAN SEE THE *CURSE* YOU PLACED UPON YOUR OWN SOUL ALL THOSE MONTHS AGO.

I DON'T BELIEVE YOU.

BE THAT AS IT MAY, WE STILL *NEED* EACH OTHER. I NEED YOU TO PROTECT MY LIVELIHOOD, AND YOU NEED ME TO PROTECT YOUR *CITY*.

THE NEXT TIME I SENSE WE ARE IN DANGER, *YOU* WILL BE THE FIRST TO KNOW. I'VE LEARNED FROM MY MISTAKE. LET ME HELP YOU.

PLEASE.

WEDNESDAY, OCTOBER 9, 2002

ABOUT TIME. YOU SCORE?

TEN BUCKS FROM AN NYU BITCH AND HALF A McMUFFIN.

EGG OR SAUSAGE?

SAUSAGE.

BARF.

YOU'RE THE PICKIEST HOMELESS DUDE I'VE EVER MET.

WE'RE NOT HOMELESS, BART. WE'RE SQUATTERS.

THERE'S A DIFFERENCE.

YES, ONE IS *FZZT* ILLEGAL.

AHN!

YO!

QUIET.

clik

DAMN. BROKEN. ≥KRRKL≤ TAKE YOUR FRIEND AND LEAVE.

AND... AND GO WHERE? THIS IS MY HOME!

NOT ANYMORE.

WHAT THE FUCK? WHO MADE YOU KING OF NEW YORK?

I WAS MADE BY THE ENGINEER...

TUESDAY, JULY 26, 1977

OCTOBER 10, 2002

COMMISH, IT'S BOUDOIR.

ONLY TOOK ABOUT A THOUSAND FAKE MUGGINGS, BUT IT PAID OFF. WHATEVER THIS THING WAS, WE *BROKE* IT.

CHRIST IN HEAVEN, IT'S *REAL?* ALL RIGHT, DON'T FUCKING TOUCH IT UNTIL THE BOMB SQUAD SHOWS UP TO--

FWOOM

HO, SHIT!

¿SKZZ¿

RAY, IT'S ME.

MY TICKET JUST GOT CALLED, BELIEVE IT OR NOT, SO I'M GOING TO HAVE TO SURRENDER MY CELL PHONE UNTIL I GET STRIKED.

WELL, THE ENTIRE COUNTRY IS WATCHING, SO TRY TO LAND A CASE THAT DOESN'T MAKE THE CITY LOOK LIKE *SHIT*.

I *WON'T* GET PICKED! BESIDES, IT'S NOT EVEN A CRIMINAL CASE, SO IT'S NOT LIKE I'D BE DEALING WITH A TRIPLE HOMICIDE OR ANYTHING.

ANYWAY, I'LL SWING BY YOUR OFFICE AFTER I GET DISCHARGED.

FOR NOW, I WANT YOU TO KEEP CHECKING IN WITH FELIX VALBY'S PAROLE OFFICER, MAKE SURE THAT SCUM-BAG IS KEEPING OUT OF--

MR. MAYOR! YOU REPORTING TO 109, TOO?

SORRY TO BOTHER YOU, SIR.

EASY BENSON, SERVED IN THE FIRST GULF WAR. JUST WANTED TO THANK YOU FOR EVERY-THING YOU DID FOR OUR BOYS IN *AFGHANISTAN* LAST YEAR.

SORRY, MR. BENSON, YOU MUST BE MISTAKEN. THE LAST TIME I LEFT THE STATES WAS A TRIP TO NIAGARA FALLS WHEN I WAS *NINE*.

UH, NO, YOUR HONOR.

DAMN STRAIGHT.

IN THIS ROOM, THERE'S ONLY ONE "YOUR HONOR," AND IT AIN'T YOU TODAY, UNDERSTOOD?

YOU'RE NOT GOING TO PICK *HIM*, ARE YOU?

THE MAYOR?

HE'S A HUGE SUPPORTER OF CONSUMER RIGHTS, BARB. HE'S A *SLAM DUNK*.

YOU ARE NOT PICKING THE FLYING MAN, ARE YOU?

THE MAYOR?

HE'S A BIG BACKER OF SMALL BUSINESS, MR. OH. HE'S A *LOCK*.

SEMPER FI, BROTHER. I CAN FEEL IT. WE'RE BOTH GOING *IN*.

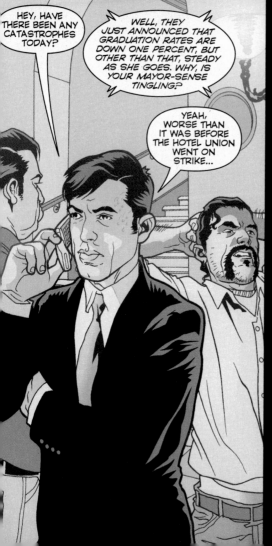

I MEAN THAT "ROBOTS" DO NOT *BLEED.*

WHO'S THE BRUISER WITH THE RUSSIAN, MA'AM?

THAT'S BRADBURY, HUNDRED'S HEAD OF SECURITY.

YOU THINK *THEY* HAVE SOMETHING TO DO WITH THIS?

I DOUBT IT, BUT I'M PRETTY SURE THEY'LL AT LEAST *LEAD* US TO OUR MAN.

AND THEN WHAT? WE GIVE 'EM A COMMENDATION FOR DOING OUR LEG-WORK *FOR* US?

NO, KURSON, WE KILL TWO BIRDS. HUNDRED'S SIDEKICKS ARE NOTHING BUT SELF-RIGHTEOUS *MERCENARIES,* INTERFERING WITH A POLICE INVESTIGATION.

THIS IS OUR CHANCE TO SEND THEM *AND* WHOEVER'S BEHIND THIS ROBOT BULLSHIT UP THE GODDAMN *RIVER,* SHOW THE REST OF THE CITY WHAT WE DO TO *ANYONE* WHO THINKS THEY'RE ABOVE THE FUCKING LAW.

BEEN A WHILE SINCE I DONE *THIS.*

THURSDAY, OCTOBER 10, 2002

I STILL THINK WE SHOULD HAVE GOTTEN THE *LAW* INVOLVED, KREMLIN.

IT TAKES A VIGILANTE TO *CATCH* A VIGILANTE. THE AUTHORITIES WOULD ONLY GET IN OUR WAY.

WE'RE SUPPOSED TO BE *RETIRED* FROM THAT LINE OF WORK. IF YOU'RE WRONG ABOUT THIS, WE'RE *EFFED.*

YOU HAVE FIVE SECONDS TO SHOW ME A WARRANT.

MAKE NO SUDDEN MOVES, RAYMOND.

KREMLIN? IS...IS THIS A PRACTICAL JOKE? DID *MITCH* PUT YOU UP TO THIS?

WE'RE, UH, ON OFFICIAL BUSINESS ON BEHALF OF THE CITY, COUNSELOR. NOW WHAT'S *THIS* ALL ABOUT?

IT'S NOT *STOLEN*, IF THAT'S WHAT YOU'RE ASKING.

I BOUGHT IT FOR OUR MUTUAL *BOSS*. MAYOR HUNDRED'S BEEN LOOKING FOR AN *ADVENTURE #265* FOR YEARS NOW.

WHY?

JESUS, THIS *IS* A JOKE, RIGHT?

I MEAN, IT WAS SUPPOSED TO BE A *GIFT*. BEFORE YOUR... *FALLING OUT*, MITCHELL WAS ALWAYS TRYING TO FIND A COPY FOR *YOU*, KREMLIN.

HE SAID YOU LEARNED ENGLISH FROM COMIC BOOKS...THAT YOU ALWAYS LIKED THIS ONE.

THE BOY IS AN *IDIOT*. ALL OF THOSE STORIES WERE THE SAME TO ME.

WELL, I'D TAKE IT BACK TO LETO'S, BUT THE GUY SOLD HIS COMIC STORE RIGHT AFTER HE GAVE ME THAT THING.

WHATEVER, I THOUGHT IF I FOUND A COPY FOR MITCH, MAYBE HE'D USE IT AS AN EXCUSE TO FINALLY *RECONCILE* WITH YOU. I CAN'T STAND SEEING YOU TWO--

OF COURSE. THAT IS ALL MY COMPANION AND I NEED.

COME, LIVES ARE ON THE LINE.

WAIT! BRADBURY, RIGHT?

THIS IS INSANE. MITCH IS *MY* FRIEND, TOO. WHATEVER'S GOING ON, IF YOU GUYS WOULD JUST LET ME INTO YOUR LITTLE SECRET SOCIETY, I...I COULD *HELP*.

YOU WANT INTO THE SECRET SOCIETY, THEN KEEP A FUCKIN' SECRET...

...AND PRETEND WE WERE NEVER HERE.

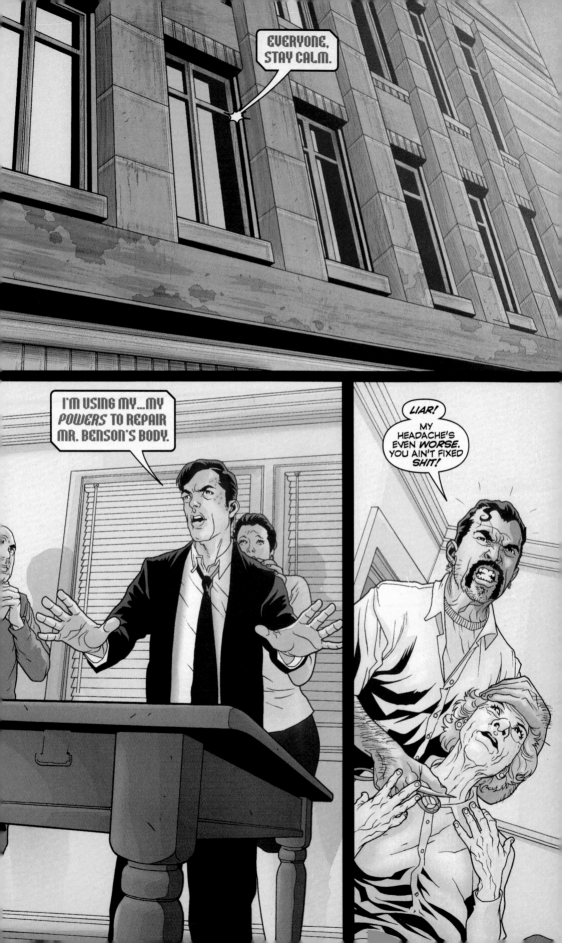

HOOONK

GODDAMMIT, PICK IT UP, CHIEF. WE LOST BRADBURY'S VAN THREE BLOCKS AGO.

PERILS OF FOLLOWING FROM THIS MANY CAR LENGTHS, MA'AM. I DON'T UNDERSTAND WHY WE DIDN'T JUST ARREST THEM BACK AT THAT SHARK'S PLACE.

BECAUSE, I DON'T WANT HUNDRED'S OLD CREW TO KNOW THEY'RE BEING SHADOWED YET.

WE WAIT UNTIL THEY FIND OUR NEW *FLYBOY*, THEN WE START MIRANDIZING THE LOT OF THEM FOR INTERFERING WITH POLICE BUSINESS.

DIAL 311

؟KKRRK؟ COMM, IF YOU'RE ON, SWITCH TO ELEVEN, PLEASE ؟KRZZT؟

THIS IS ANGOTTI.

COMMISSIONER, IT'S HOLLIDAY WITH MIDTOWN NORTH. IS THE MAYOR STILL AT THE COURTHOUSE?

I GUESS, BUT I'M NOT HIS FUCKING PERSONAL ASSISTANT. WHY, WHAT'S UP?

TEN MINUTES AGO, ALL THE NEWS TICKERS IN TIMES SQUARE STARTED REPEATING THE SAME MESSAGE.

IT'S SUPPOSEDLY FROM *MAYOR HUNDRED.* SAYS THAT HE'S INVOLVED IN A *HOSTAGE SITUATION* INSIDE A DELIBERATING ROOM AT 60 CENTRE.

BULLSHIT. THAT BUILDING'S FIFTY BLOCKS AWAY FROM YOU. HUNDRED MIGHT BE A FREAK, BUT HE CAN'T TALK ACROSS THE CITY. IT'S A PRANK.

MAYOR HUNDRED TRANSMITT
EMERGENCY INSTR
NEED TACTICAL S

MAYOR HUNDRED TR
EMERGENCY INSTR
NEED TACTICAL S

I DON'T KNOW, MA'AM. THE TECH WONKS AT ALL THE NEWS DESK'S SAY THOSE SIGNS ARE A CLOSED SYSTEM, SO THEY CAN'T HAVE BEEN *HACKED.*

AND I TRIED CALLING THE MAYOR'S HEAD OF SECURITY, BUT HE'S NOT ANSWERING HIS CELL.

CHRIST. ALL RIGHT, TURN THIS BOAT AROUND, KURSON. WHATEVER HUNDRED'S GOONS ARE UP TO...

...THEY'RE ON THEIR OWN NOW.

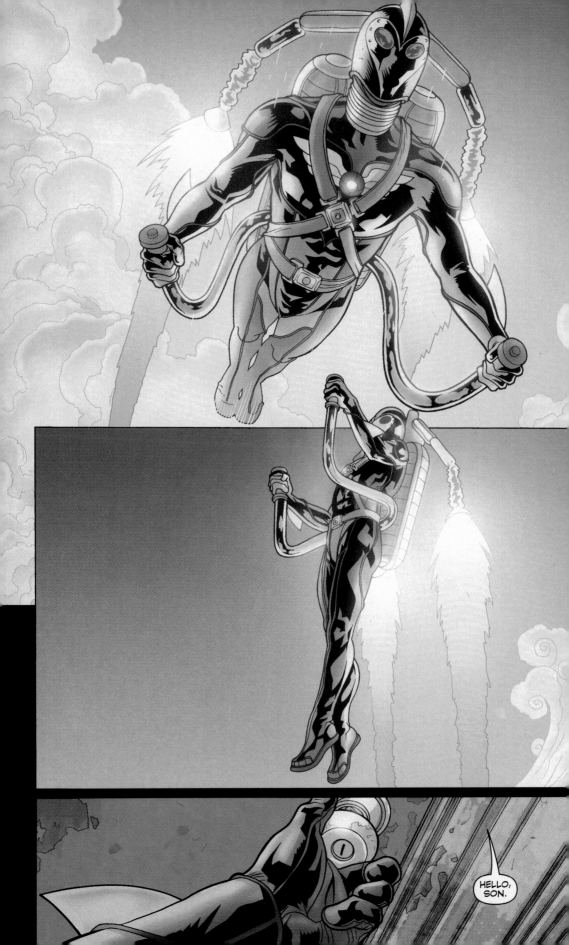

HELLO, SON.

ANF!

WHAT'S *WRONG* WITH YOU PEOPLE!

I'M JUST TRYING TO *HELP!*

THAT'S *ENOUGH!*

DON'T BOTHER, OLD MAN.

IN CASE YOU HAVEN'T NOTICED, I'M SORTA *BULLET-PROOF.*

BULLETS ARE FOR *ASSHOLES.*

WEDNESDAY, JULY 2, 1986

TUESDAY, JULY 25, 2000

THURSDAY, NOVEMBER 7, 2002

I'M SO SORRY, HONEY.

I'M...I'M IN A BAD WAY HERE.

MOM, WHERE *ARE* YOU?

...WHAT?

I SCREWED UP BAD.

BUT I'M... I'M SO PROUD OF...NN...

DIGITAL SWITCHBOARD, WHERE'S SHE CALLING FROM?

YOU HAVE REACHED A PRIVATE NUMBER.

BYPASS.

CELLULAR CARRIER. NO ADDITIONAL INFORMATION IS AVAILABLE AT THIS TIME.

THREE... TWO...ONE... IGNITION.

VRYYYYYYYYY

AHHH!

HOW... HOW DID YOU...?

GET IN YOUR RIG, AND TAKE HER OUT FOR A DRIVE.

A LONG ONE.

MOM?

HELLO, MITCHELL.

I MISS ANYTHING *EXCITING* SINCE I LEFT THE BIG CITY?

MONDAY, DECEMBER 15, 1969

NOVEMBER 7, 2002

THIS DOESN'T MAKE ANY SENSE. I'VE READ ALL THE REPORTS. THEY PULLED DAD'S BODY OUT OF A *CAVE-IN*.

THAT'S JUST HOW THEY MADE IT LOOK.

"THEY?"

YOUR FATHER'S FRIENDS, THE OTHER SANDHOGS HE WORKED WITH.

THEY WERE LIKE BROTHERS TO HIM. AFTER I CALLED, THEY PICKED UP HIS BODY AND BROUGHT IT BACK TO THE TUNNELS THAT NIGHT.

WHY? MOM, IT...IT WAS AN *ACCIDENT*. IF WHAT YOU'RE SAYING IS TRUE, YOU WERE JUST *DEFENDING* YOURSELF.

WAS THAT WHAT I WAS SUPPOSED TO TELL YOUR *GRANDPARENTS?* THAT THEIR SON DIED TRYING TO *STRANGLE* HIS WIFE TO DEATH?

I WASN'T GOING TO KILL THOSE PEOPLE, TOO.

BESIDES, I HAD *YOU* TO THINK ABOUT.

IF YOUR FATHER DIED AT HOME, WE GOT NOTHING. BUT IF HE DIED IN THE LINE OF DUTY...

SO WHAT, HIS PALS TOOK HIM DOWN THERE AND *BLEW HIM UP?* SO YOU COULD GET A *PENSION?*

IT'S WHAT YOUR FATHER WOULD HAVE WANTED.

CUT IT OUT!

VRRRRRR

VRRRRRRRR--*

SO I WAS RAISED WITH *BLOOD MONEY?* TAKEN FROM THE CITY I *RUN* NOW? MOM, THESE *MEN.* THE ONES WHO HELPED YOU...

THEY WERE DIGGERS, MITCHELL. IF ACCIDENTS DIDN'T GET 'EM, LUNG DISEASE DID. THEY'RE ALL GONE NOW, AND THEY TOOK THIS WITH THEM.

YOU DON'T HAVE TO WORRY ABOUT THE TRUTH COMING BACK TO *HAUNT* YOU. YOU'RE THE ONLY OTHER PERSON I'VE EVER TOLD.

WHY?

WHY *NOW?*

YOU THINK I DON'T OWN A *TELEVISION?* YOU THINK EVERY NEW *ASSASSINATION ATTEMPT* AGAINST YOU DOESN'T *TEAR ME APART?*

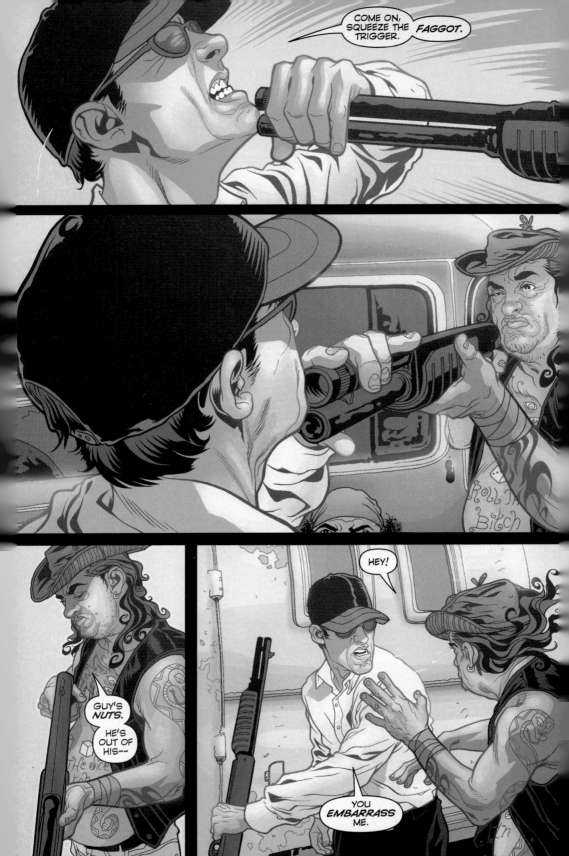

SO, YOU KIDS USING SUPER 8 OR 16MM?

UH, WE'RE ACTUALLY SHOOTING DV, MR. MAYOR.

VIDEO?

HOW DO THEY GET AWAY WITH CALLING IT FILM SCHOOL IF YOU NEVER ACTUALLY USE *FILM?*

THANKS AGAIN FOR LETTING THESE GUYS CHECK OUT THE WATER TUNNEL, SIR.

NAH, YOU WERE RIGHT, JOURNAL. NEW YORKERS DESERVE TO KNOW WHAT'S HAPPENING DOWN HERE. WITHOUT TRANSPARENCY AT EVERY LEVEL, A CITY *COLLAPSES.*

DIDN'T YOUR *DAD* WORK ON THIS THING, MAYOR HUNDRED?